Kase for the Environment

Publisher: Wayne Morgan   www.zirklepress.com
Photographer: Wayne Morgan   www.waynemorganartistry.com
Author: Dink NeSmith   dnesmith@cninewspapers.com
Illustrator: Mack Williams www.mackwilliams.com
Editors: Lynn S. Rice
        Phil Hudgins
Design and Layout: Ryan Harris   www.rzkharris.com

Zirkle Press, LLC
89 Pat Harris Road
Nahunta, GA 31553 USA

Wayne Morgan
(912) 462-6590
(912) 288-0810
email: wmorganphoto@hotmail.com
wayne@waynemorganartistry.com
website : www.waynemorganartistry.com
        www.zirklepress.com

Printed and Bound by: Four Colour Print Group and Lifetouch Commercial Printing
Loves Park, IL USA
www.fourcolour.com

November 2012
6 7 6 7 4 . 5

Printed in the United States of America

Hardcover ISBN: 978-0-615-70956-7
Library of Congress control number: 2012951099

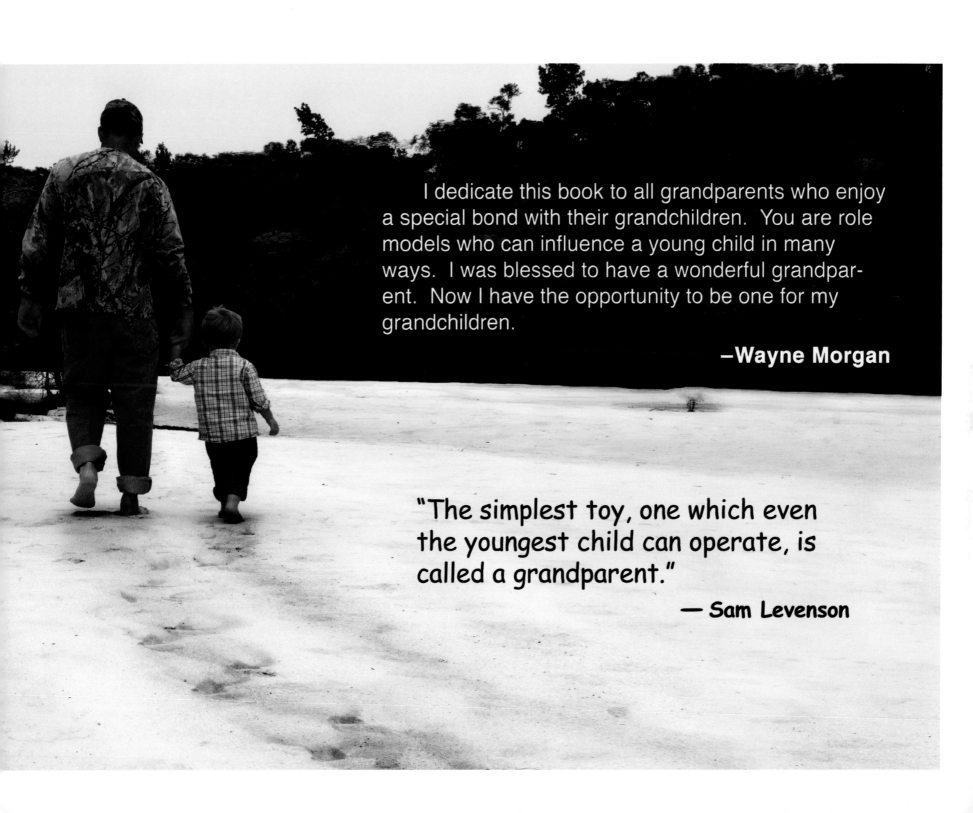

I dedicate this book to all grandparents who enjoy a special bond with their grandchildren. You are role models who can influence a young child in many ways. I was blessed to have a wonderful grandparent. Now I have the opportunity to be one for my grandchildren.

–Wayne Morgan

"The simplest toy, one which even the youngest child can operate, is called a grandparent."

— Sam Levenson

Kase for the Environment

Hello, I'm Kase.

I can't wait until Saturday.

Today is just Monday, and Saturday seems as far away as the moon.

But I have to wait, because Saturday is Satilla Day—Satilla River Day. And that is the day I love most because Papa, my mommy's daddy, takes me to the Satilla.

What is the Satilla?

Have you heard of Disney World?

Well, we don't have one of those in Georgia, but we do have a river that is a fun place to go. I'd rather be squishing my toes in the sugary-white sandbars of the Satilla River than be anywhere in the world.

Would you like to come with Papa and me to see this magical place?

OK.

Let's go.

Yellow-bellied Slider Turtle

1

I hope you don't mind getting up early. Papa and I leave his house when it is still dark outside.

We drive down sandy roads with big trees all around. Sometimes Papa stops his truck and rolls down the windows.

We can hear crickets and other critters making noises as they wake up, too.

But we don't wait too long. Papa likes to take pictures of the sun coming up over the river.

Young Great Horned Owl

2

And you know what?

The Satilla River water is shiny black. Papa says it's from leaves and natural things that fall into the water. And it's like a mirror. Sometimes I just look at the water and stare. I see me, looking back at me.

Bird Grasshopper

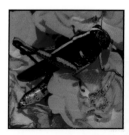

3

River Otter

And you know who else I see?

I see Papa kneeling behind me and smiling. Papa is always smiling with me at the Satilla.

Well, almost always smiling. One time, I saw him sad. He was so sad I thought he was going to cry. I'll tell you about that later. Right now, let's take a look around the river.

4

Look! There's a raccoon. Did you know raccoons always wash their food before they eat? And see that otter poking his head out of the river? See his shiny head and whiskers? And there's another one, standing on the bank. I tell Papa that otters are the silliest critters in the Satilla. They do funny tricks, swimming with their long tails.

Gray Squirrel

5

When we come to the river, we almost always see alligators. Some are big, really big. Look! There's one over there, just nosing around in the shade. Papa says from the size of its nose, he thinks that gator is about eight feet long. I wouldn't want to be swimming with him!

**Mallard Duck,
Male**

6

And we see tiny gators, too. Look! There's a mommy gator on the bank. Can you believe it? A baby gator is crawling around in its mommy's mouth. I heard that baby gators do that when they sense danger.

Young Great Egret

7

There are lots of wildlife families along the Satilla River, like these cattle egrets. Sometimes we see birds flying. But most of the time, they are just sitting on limbs, watching us creep by in Papa's boat.

Gray Fox

8

Just like my mommy cooks for me,
~~~irds feed their little ones, too.

Eastern Bluebird

9

Papa's boat has a quiet motor, so we can slip down the river without making much noise or waves to disturb the mirror-like waters. See the reflection of the cypress trees in the water?

Some of these trees were growing along the Satilla when Christopher Columbus discovered America 500 years ago. Can you believe it?

Squirrel Tree Frog

10

With Papa's long lens on his camera, we can see things far away. He lets me look. There's a corn snake wrapped around a cypress knee. Over there is a gray fox looking at us while we are looking at him.

Gopher Tortoise

11

In the fall, before Thanksgiving, the leaves on the trees change from green to bright colors and reflect in the black water of the Satilla.

Baby Yellow-crowned Night Heron

12

In the spring, when leaves start to turn green again, you can hear and see turkey gobblers strutting along the banks. Papa says the boy turkeys are showing off for the girl turkeys.

Monarch Butterfly

13

Northern Cardinal

14

There are really two Satilla rivers, Big Satilla and Little Satilla. Let's take a peek at Little Satilla. Get ready. Before long, we'll visit Papa's favorite and most magical place on the river. It's called Zirkle. But first, look at the white sandbar under the tea-colored water of the Little Satilla. The water is low right now.

And when the water is low, you can see lots of things. See! Those circles in the sand are fish beds. Papa says fish use their tails to fan out round beds on the river bottom. That's where they lay their eggs to hatch more fish. Get ready. We're almost at Zirkle.

Bluegill Bream

15

**Nesting
Great Egret**

16

We're here! One hundred years ago, Zirkle was a tiny town on the Little Satilla River. About 300 people lived there. They were loggers who cut trees and floated them to a sawmill to make lumber. Today, no one lives at Zirkle except critters and lots of mosquitoes. The mosquitoes are always buzzing around our heads, but Papa loves to visit Zirkle.

All that is left are pieces of rusty metal and wooden dams. Water swishes through the cracks and swirls into the river. Papa can take pictures in a special way to make the water at Zirkle magical-looking.

Bald Eagle

17

Squirrel
Tree Frog

When we go to the Satilla, we like to go slow, poking around like the gopher tortoise. If we don't hurry, we can see more things around us. Papa says the gopher tortoise is endangered, which means too many are dying. Their habitat, where they live, is being destroyed by people. How would you like for someone to knock down your house?

18

That's what's happening to the pileated woodpeckers, too. There are fewer places left for these red-headed woodpeckers to live, but I'm glad they are still at home along the Satilla.

White-tailed Deer

19

Just like Papa, the gopher tortoises and pileated woodpeckers, I am at home on the Satilla, too. I love watching birds fish, and I think they like watching me fish, too.

Mallard Duck,
Female

20

One day, when we were in Papa's creek boat, I said, "Look!" We stopped the boat and I climbed onto Papa's shoulders, while he took pictures of big birds.

North American Millipede

21

Pileated Woodpecker

There they were—big wood storks. Look at those wings. And look at their heads. Papa says wood storks are so ugly, they are almost cute. Ugl or cute, I like to watch wood storks.

22

Papa likes to look for unusual things like these tree roots dipping their toes into the Satilla River. I said they looked like worms, wiggling and trying to get in the water.

Young Northern Mockingbird

23

I think I like frogs best. Frogs are every-
where on the Satilla. Sometimes they are sitting on
lily pads.

Great Blue Heron

24

Other times, they are stretched
ut like this one, taking a nap—or may-
e he's just waiting for a bug to crawl
y. Once I scared my mommy. I heard
her yell, "Eeeeeeeeekkk!" She found the
frog that I put in my pocket. I promised I
wouldn't do that again.

Baby American
Alligator

25

Papa says I am always hungry. He keeps snacks, not frogs, in his pocket for me. We saw nests of baby birds that were hungry, too. They were cry-ing, "Mommy, feed me!"

River Frog

26

I bet this Great Blue Heron and this grasshopper were thinking, "What's for supper tonight?" And I wonder if the heron was thinking, "How about a grasshopper?"

Barred Owl

27

Papa said, "Over there, Kase. It's a pretty butterfly." I got a quick glance before it fluttered away. Somethi[ng] scared it.

Great Egret

Two egrets were making a racket. Papa said, "Let's get out of the boat and go see what that's all about."

"Really, you won't believe it," the birds seemed to say.

Gulf Fritillary Butterfly

29

Oh, no! This is what I warned you about. This is what makes Papa so sad that I think he is going to cry. I don't ever want to see Papa cry, not at our favorite place, the Satilla River. People camped here on the sandbar and left their trash. I covered my eyes. I didn't like seeing it.

Wood Stork

30

If people love coming to the Satilla as much as Papa and I do, then why wouldn't they just pick up their trash and take it with them? It would be so easy to do that. Look at this stuff. It makes Papa and me sad and angry.

Red-tailed Hawk

31

Even though I am a little boy, I know what is right and wrong. People scattering junk in and around the river is just wrong, wrong, wrong!

Green Tree Frog

32

Look at this awful mess! Some people are ruining the Satilla. Seeing trash like tires, garbage and even toilets scattered all over the place makes Papa angry. That's why he asked me to help him write this book. He said, "Kase, you can build more Disney Worlds, but God won't give us another Satilla."

Corn Snake

33

American Alligator

34

Look what happens when lots of people toss their trash into the river. It looks like a river of floating garbage.

Would you want to fish or swim in that? No way! Doesn't this make you mad, too?

Papa says owls are wise birds. I think these owls are saying, "Whoooooo is going to help us clean up this mess?"

Northern
Raccoon

Some people are already trying to help. The Satilla flows by the city of Waycross, Georgia. The people there want to clean up the river, so they set up a special trap to catch trash that floats by. More cities could do this, but we can all help by not throwing trash in our rivers. How easy is that? We must teach people to keep our rivers and the environment clean. Clean for the wildlife and us, too.

Why are you crying, Mr. Owl?

Look, Kase! See all that trash in the river? Can't we do something to teach people not to trash our beautiful home?

Yes, we can! Papa and I are going to write a book!

Papa's pictures will show people how ugly trash makes our environment!

We'll ask them not to throw chemicals in storm drains. And we'll remind them not to litter.

We'll ask them to always clean up after themselves and maybe after other people, too

Thank you, Kase and Papa. I think your book will really help.

Kase wants you to help save the environment. Get your family to recycle paper, plastic and cans. Always put trash where it belongs--in a trash can. Keep a litter bag in the car and never throw trash out the window. Help keep playgrounds, parks and camping areas clean. Never pour paint or household chemicals on the ground or in storm drains. That makes our water and rivers polluted. Most of all, ask your friends to help, too. Working together, we can keep our environment clean and beautiful!

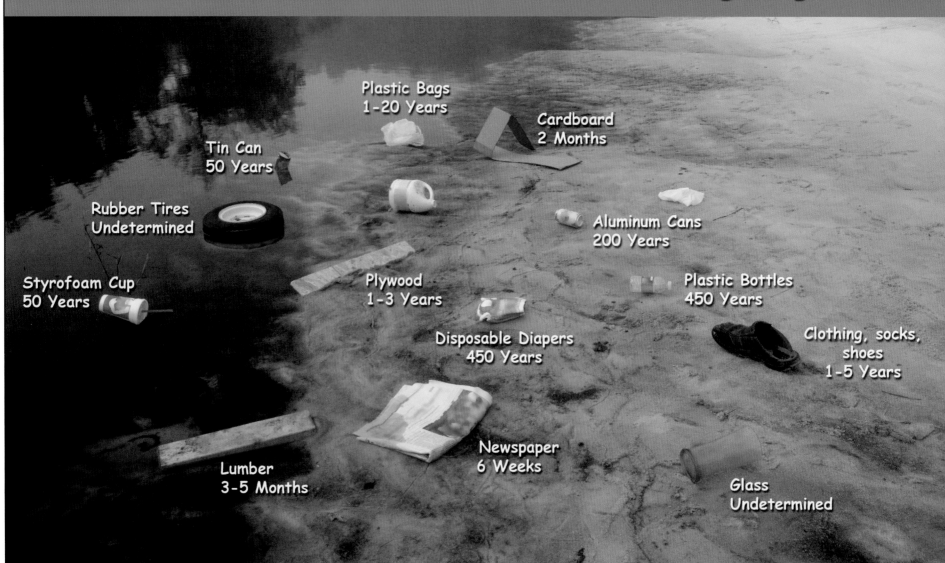

Question: How long does trash last in the environment?

Answer: A long, long time.

Plastic Bags
1-20 Years

Cardboard
2 Months

Tin Can
50 Years

Rubber Tires
Undetermined

Aluminum Cans
200 Years

Styrofoam Cup
50 Years

Plywood
1-3 Years

Plastic Bottles
450 Years

Disposable Diapers
450 Years

Clothing, socks, shoes
1-5 Years

Lumber
3-5 Months

Newspaper
6 Weeks

Glass
Undetermined

I am a lucky little boy. Papa loves me, and
he loves to take me to his magical place, the Satilla River. When I grow up, I want to be just like
Papa. I want to enjoy nature and take my grandchildren to the river. But I'm scared. What if the
beautiful Satilla River isn't beautiful anymore? I
don't want to be scared. Let's save our rivers and
our environment. Will you help?

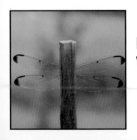

Dragonfly Wings

40

Thank you for going with Papa and me on this adventure. It's been a long, fun day. When we were loading Papa's boat into the back of his truck, he said,

"Look, Kase. See that sunset over the river? God gave us a clean, beautiful environment. I know He wants us to keep it that way."

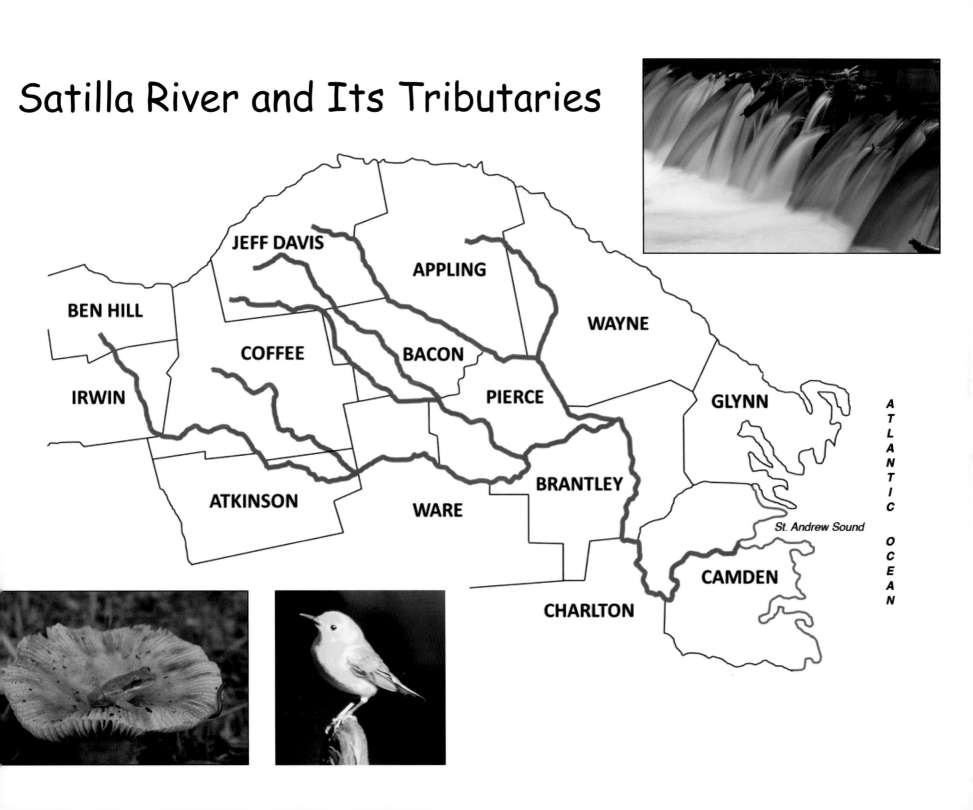

Satilla River and Its Tributaries

Dink NeSmith, a native of Jesup, Ga., is president and co-owner of Community Newspapers, Inc. The Athens, Ga.-based company publishes newspapers in Georgia, Florida and North Carolina. Dink and Pam NeSmith have three children—Alan, Emily and Eric—and six grandsons: Wyatt, Hayes, William, Henry, Fenn and Bayard. A passionate conservationist, Dink is always planning his next trip to the woods and waters of southeast Georgia, home of the Satilla River. And if he's lucky, one or more of his soon-to-be seven grandsons will go with him. His award-winning newspaper columns can be found at www.dinknesmith.com.

Wayne Morgan, born in the southeast Georgia town of Waycross, has lived his entire life in the adjoining county of Brantley. In his early years, he spent many hours hunting and fishing in and around the Satilla River. In 1999, at the age of 35, a heart condition required the installation of a pacemaker. After this period, he started trying to show the beauty of the Satilla by laying down his gun and fishing pole and picking up a camera. He has won many awards with his photography, and in 2011 published his first coffee-table book called *Satilla Solitude*. He is a conservationist who hopes to one day have the Satilla River free from the trash that he sometimes finds on his photo shoots. Wayne and his wife, Bonnie, have two children, Kristen and Kyle; three grandchildren, Kase, Braylee and Addie.

Satilla Solitude
Wayne Morgan

Wayne Morgan
Nature photographer, author and publisher

89 Pat Harris Road
Nahunta, GA 31553 USA

(912) 462-6590 or (912) 288-0810

wmorganphoto@hotmail.com
wayne@waynemorganartistry.com

www.waynemorganartistry.com
www.zirklepress.com

Wayne Morgan
ARTISTRY

Published in 2011